Get the Bell!

To Big Ben!

Written by Joanna Layland

My top fact!

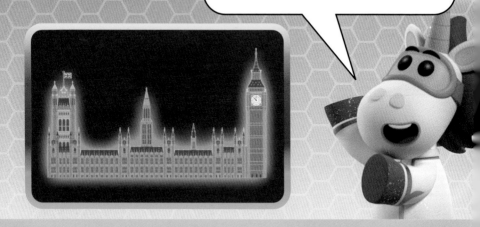

Big Ben is in the UK.

Big Ben is not the clock.
It is the bell!

3

Bots, get rid of the bell!

I must nap.

The bots get the bell
and buzz off.

Drop me off at the clock.

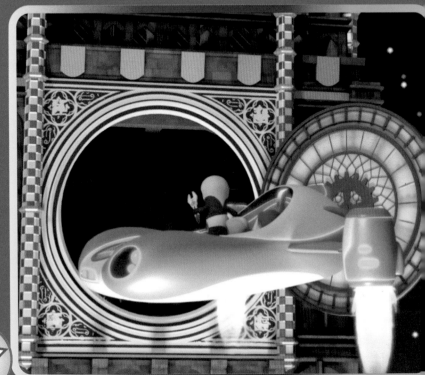

The bots' rocket is metal! My magnets can get it back!

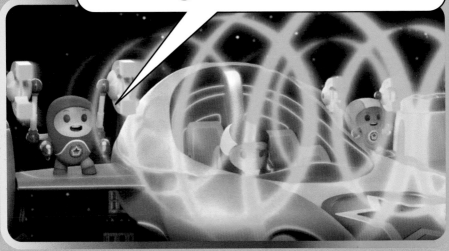

ZAP!

The bell
is back in
the clock.

I will
fix it!

No! My nap!